My Workbook for
Outsmarting Explosive Behavior

Student's Name _____

Autism Asperger Publishing Co.
P.O. Box 23173
Shawnee Mission, Kansas 66283-0173
www.asperger.net

APC

© 2009 AAPC
P.O. Box 23173
Shawnee Mission, Kansas 66283-0173
www.asperger.net • 913.897.1004

ISBN: 978-1-934575-44-4

This book is designed in Helvetica Neue.

Printed in the United States of America.

Why Am I Doing This Workbook?

If you are doing this workbook, it is because you have some behaviors that are called explosive behaviors. **Explosive behavior** is what you do or how you act when it feels like you cannot hold your insides together and they start exploding all around you. This can be scary. I know, because when I was growing up, I sometimes exploded. During those times I did things that I really felt badly about afterwards. Some of these behaviors include hitting, biting, kicking, throwing things, destroying property, etc.

I am now an adult. In fact, I have three children who are also now adults. My son Paul had lots of trouble with explosive behavior when he was growing up. Paul and I have autism. Some really good news is that we both learned how to outsmart our explosive behavior so it no longer gives us trouble.

I work with lots of children and adults who sometimes have explosive behavior. We work together to outsmart their explosive behavior so the behavior no longer gets them into trouble. If you are reading this, you probably have had explosive behaviors and someone in your life has heard about this workbook. Someone wants to team up with you to outsmart your explosive behavior so you will no longer get in trouble because of this behavior.

So, welcome to *My Workbook for Outsmarting Explosive Behavior*. I'm really glad we have found each other.

Sincerely,

Judy Endow

My Support Team

Explosive behavior is serious. It can hurt you, and it can also hurt others. Nobody wants to have this kind of behavior. If you could have solved your explosive behavior on your own, you would already have done so.

When you are exploding, the behavior is beyond your control. Therefore, it is best to have a support team to help you work on outsmarting your explosive behavior. It works best for a team to include a minimum of three people, but your team may have more than three people.

You are the number one person on your team. Even if you don't know me or can't see me, I will also be on your team and will coach you through this workbook. If someone gave you this workbook, that person may be interested in being on your team, too. Other people who might be interested in being on your team include your parents, teachers and professional helpers.

Besides you and me, you only need one other person to get started, but you may include more people on your team. Fill in as many of the following blanks as you need to show all your support team members. It is O.K. to add more lines if you have more people to include on your support team.

My support team for outsmarting explosive behavior includes:

1. _____ **(myself)**

2. _____ *Judy* _____ **(author of this workbook)**

3. _____

4. _____

5. _____

Remember to make sure that the people you would like to be on your support team have been asked and have agreed to be on your team. One way you might ask them is to show them this workbook and say, "I'm going to work on outsmarting my explosive behavior. I think you would be a good person to be on my team." You could then show the person this workbook and ask if he or she would like to be on your team after having had a chance to look over the workbook.

Sometimes people you would like to be on your support team are not able to do so. There are lots of reasons why people decide not to be on your support team. Some may tell you the reason, and others may not tell you the reason. It is O.K. if people you ask to be on your team tell you they cannot be on your team. Just say, "I'm sorry it won't work out for you, but thanks for letting me ask." You can then ask another person if you'd like.

Activity

The activity for you and your team to do before you meet again is to look over the three parts of this kit. That way you will all get an idea of what we will be doing the next several times the team gets together. You don't need to understand all the parts of this kit at this point. The activity is simply to look at each part before you get together with your team the next time.

The three parts of this kit are:

1. A facilitator manual called *Outsmarting Explosive Behavior – A Visual System of Support and Intervention for Individuals with Autism Spectrum Disorders.* This is the story and explanation of how a train with four cars is used to help outsmart explosive behavior.

2. *My Visual for Outsmarting Explosive Behavior*. This is a visual system consisting of a fold-out train board along with little stop, go and yield signs.

3. This workbook, called *My Workbook for Outsmarting Explosive Behavior*. As you and your team complete this workbook, you will be constructing your own train model that will show you and others just how to outsmart your explosive behavior.

I'm Having a Great Day and
Plan to Keep It That Way!

It is helpful for you to know about yourself how things are when you are having a great day and are feeling calm with no worries at all. Write or draw your answers below. The cartoon on the next page may start you thinking.

When I am having a great day, feeling calm and with no worries at all ...

- When people look at me, they will see:

  _____

  _____

  _____

  _____

  _____

  _____

- Inside of me it looks and feels like:

  _____

  _____

  _____

  _____

  _____

  _____

  _____

When I am having a great day,
my train is in the station.

It is not going anywhere!
This is a good thing!

I don't want my train to start running.
I like feeling calm and having no worries.

Feeling calm and having no worries is the "just right" way to be. There are lots of things you can do every day to help you stay in your just right place. A fancy name for these helpful things is Regulation Strategies. This includes sensory regulation strategies that you find helpful. Regulation means doing something to stay in your just right place. Strategies are the things that you do.

My Regulation Strategies that help me stay in my just right place include:

_____

_____

_____

_____

_____

_____

_____

_____

_____

_____

_____

_____

People with autism have brains that are wired differently than the brains of people without autism. The way a brain is wired is sometimes called neurology. Because we have autism, we have a different neurology than others. This means that we need to plan for staying regulated. Making plans to stay regulated is one way we can take charge and outsmart our autism neurology and our unwanted behavior. Our plans are called Support Strategies.

Having an autism neurology also means that we are wired to crave predictability, sameness and routine. People with autism tend to stay better regulated the more the world around them offers them predictability, sameness and routine. Each person with autism has his or her preferences about which predictability, sameness and routine supports work best.

My Support Strategies for predictability, sameness and routine that help me stay in my just right place include:

_____

_____

_____

_____

_____

_____

_____

_____

_____

_____

_____

Activity

First, look in the Facilitator Manual to see the example of Paul's Train and How It Runs. Notice the first group of stop signs for Paul's train on page 15. This group of stop signs represents Paul's Support Strategies. Some of the words on Paul's stop signs may be like the words in your list of Support Strategies. Everybody who makes a behavior train will have some parts that are the same and some parts that are different from others who have already made a train.

Sometimes people get good ideas for their own train by looking at someone else's train. If you get any good ideas when you look at Paul's train, it is perfectly fine to use them for your train. In the same way, others may come to use some of your ideas if they make a train. It is good to share helpful ideas this way.

Next, get out *My Visual for Outsmarting Explosive Behavior*. You will be making the first group of stop signs for your behavior train. Look at the red box on page 5 of this workbook where you listed your Regulation Strategies. Write each Regulation Strategy on a separate stop sign. If a Regulation Strategy is too long to fit on the stop sign, sum up the idea in a few words so the words will fit onto the stop sign.

Now, look at the red box on page 6 of this workbook where you listed your Support Strategies. Write each Support Strategy on a separate stop sign. If a Support Strategy is too wordy to fit onto the stop sign, sum up the idea in a few words so the words will fit onto the stop sign.

Finally, put all the finished stop signs in the first pocket on the visual labeled Positive Interventions.

Here is an example of how your visual will look. Your stop signs will show your Support Strategies so you will have as many stop signs as it takes to show your strategies. This may be more stop signs or fewer stop signs than shown in the example.

Paul's Train and How It Runs

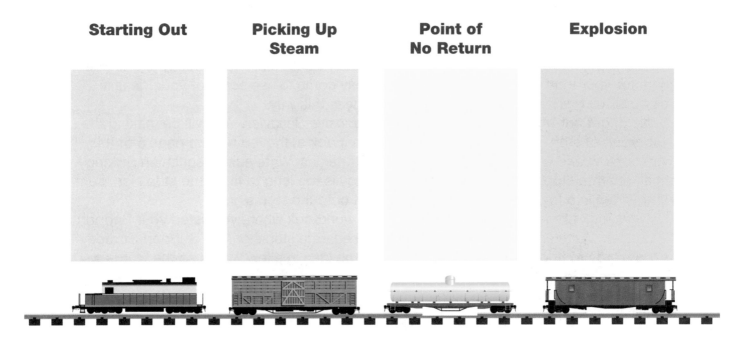

Starting Out	Picking Up Steam	Point of No Return	Explosion

Whenever you do something written on one of the stop signs, you can take that stop sign out of the pocket and place it in front of the train engine. This shows that you are using the strategy on the stop sign to prevent the train from starting out.

_____'s Train and How It Runs

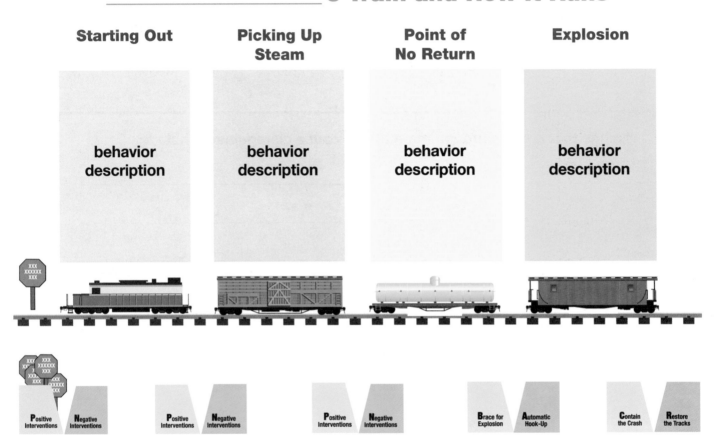

You can even plan out ahead of time which stop sign you will use to outsmart your train so it doesn't start out. Use your stop signs to outsmart your autism in a way that works well for you. The more you use the stop signs, the better you will get at outsmarting your behavior and the more often you will be in your just right calm place, having a great day and keeping it that way.

Sometimes I'm Having a Great Day and Then I Start to Get Disregulated

Sometimes you are well regulated (having a great day, feeling calm and having no worries). You plan out and use your stop signs in a way that works well for you. Then something happens that causes you to start to become disregulated. You start to feel a bit out of sorts, perhaps a little fussy. When this happens, your calm, just right feeling starts slipping away.

Things that happen around me that can cause disregulation include:

_____

_____

_____

_____

_____

_____

_____

_____

_____

_____

_____

Sometimes you are having a great day. You plan out and use your stop signs in a way that works well for you. You are going along in your day doing just fine and then someone does something that can start to make you feel fussy inside! When this happens, you know that you are becoming disregulated.

Most often this has to do with somebody springing a surprise on you, interrupting a routine or expecting that you will respond immediately to whatever they want you to do. When you start to feel fussy, you can usually keep it inside, and most of the time people may not even know that they are doing something that is causing you to become disregulated.

Things people do that can cause disregulation include:

_____

_____

_____

_____

_____

_____

_____

_____

_____

_____

_____

_____

Activity

First, get out *My Visual for Outsmarting Explosive Behavior*. You will be making the first group of go signs for your behavior train. Look at the green box on page 10 of this workbook where you listed things that happen around you that can cause disregulation. Write each of these things on a separate go sign. If an item is too wordy to fit onto the go sign, sum up the idea in a few words so the words will fit onto the sign.

Next, look at the green box on page 11 of this workbook where you listed things that people do that can cause disregulation. Write each of these things on a separate go sign. If an item is too long to fit onto the go sign, sum up the idea in a few words so the words will fit onto the sign.

You may look in the Facilitator Manual (page 18) to see the example of Paul's behavior train. Please feel free to use anything that might apply to your situation.

Finally, put all the finished go signs in the first pocket on the visual labeled Negative Interventions. Your train will now look similar to this. You might have more signs or fewer signs than pictured in the example, and that is O.K. Each person has the number of signs he needs to show his situation.

_____'s Train and How It Runs

Starting Out	Picking Up Steam	Point of No Return	Explosion

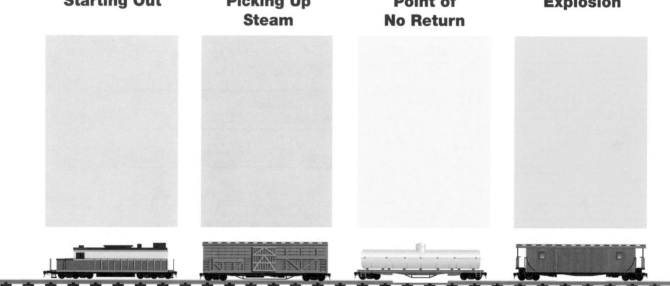

You can use your go signs to outsmart your behavior in a way that works well for you. For example, if something starts happening that makes you feel a little fussy or a bit disregulated, you can take that go sign out of the pocket and place it in front of the train engine.

If you do not have a go sign already made to show what is causing you to begin to feel disregulated, you can make a new go sign to show it. In fact, the more you work with this model, the more things you will discover to write on the signs! It is always O.K. to make new signs for your behavior train.

_____'s Train and How it Runs

Starting Out	Picking Up Steam	Point of No Return	Explosion

Show someone on your team (or someone who understands your train model) what is happening. Show them the go sign that is causing you to feel fussy or to become disregulated and ask them to help you manage that go sign.

Starting Out
Behavior Description

    Sometimes you will be able to quickly get back to having a great day and feeling well regulated. Other times this will not be so, and your train will start out. It is important that you and those who support you know exactly what it looks like when your train is Starting Out.

When my train is Starting Out, people looking at me will see:

_____

_____

_____

_____

_____

_____

When my train is Starting Out, inside me I feel:

_____

_____

_____

_____

_____

_____

Activity

First, look at the example of Paul's Starting Out behavior in the Facilitator Manual (page 19).

Next, use your descriptions from the sections you just completed in this workbook to write your behaviors on the light blue square above the train engine. If you have a lot of words in your description, you may need to condense them to fit into the square.

Finally, know that some people prefer to write their description on a sticky note and fit the sticky note to the Starting Out square. You may either write your behavior description directly onto the light blue Starting Out square or onto a sticky note to put on the light blue square.

_____'s Train and How It Runs

Starting Out	Picking Up Steam	Point of No Return	Explosion

| Positive Interventions | Negative Interventions | Positive Interventions | Negative Interventions | Positive Interventions | Negative Interventions | Brace for Explosion | Automatic Hook-Up | Contain the Crash | Restore the Tracks |

At this point it will probably be helpful for you to look at the workbook through to the end. By looking through the rest of this workbook, you will see how the behavior stages are laid out and the intervention levels that go after each behavior stage.

Most people who have explosive behavior know what their behavior looks like in the Explosion stage and choose to start with the Explosion section of the workbook. After you look through the rest of the workbook, choose the section that matches what you know best about your explosive behavior. Fill in that section. Talk to your support team. Together, you will come up with a plan to learn about your explosive behavior cycle in a way that will allow you to complete this workbook and your behavior train model.

It is O.K. if you do not know all the information you need to fill in this workbook. Just fill in what you do know and start to use it. Over time you will discover and learn even more about yourself. As that happens, you can fill in more of the workbook.

Please remind yourself often:

I am a good person

working on ways

to outsmart

my explosive behavior.

Starting Out
Interventions

    As you probably already know, once your behavior and feelings are those in your Starting Out phase, the strategies that normally help keep you regulated no longer work very well. This is common with most people who have explosive behavior. It is a good thing to know about yourself.

    Now that you know this, you can stop trying so hard to use the usual strategies. It will work better for you to zero in on the strategies that *do* work for you when you are in the Starting Out phase. That way, once you are in the Starting Out phase, you and those who support you can move up to this next level of interventions.

Positive Strategies that work well for me once I am in the Starting Out phase include:

_____

_____

_____

_____

_____

_____

_____

_____

_____

_____

_____

Sometimes people who have explosive behaviors find it difficult to find the words that go on their stop signs. If that happens for you, it is O.K. It is often easier to look around and see what is going wrong around you. You might try doing this. The things going wrong are the Negative Strategies that are working against you. These can include things that are happening around you or things that others may be saying or doing.

Negative Strategies that work against me once I am in the Starting Out phase include:

_____

_____

_____

_____

_____

_____

_____

_____

_____

_____

_____

_____

Activity

First, get out *My Visual for Outsmarting Explosive Behavior*. You will now be making the second group of stop and go signs for your behavior train. Write each of the things you wrote in the red box on page 18 on a separate stop sign. If an item is too long to fit on the stop sign, sum up the idea in a few words so the words will fit onto the stop sign.

Next, write each of the things you wrote in the green box on page 19 on a separate go sign. If an item is too long to fit on the go sign, sum up the idea in a few words so the words will fit onto the go sign.

You may look in the Facilitator Manual (page 27) to see the example of Paul's behavior train. Again, please feel free to use anything that may apply to your situation.

Finally, put all the finished stop signs in the second pocket on the visual labeled Positive Interventions. Then put all the finished go signs in the second pocket on the visual labeled Negative Interventions.

Your train will now look similar to this. Each person has different numbers of stop and go signs. That is O.K. You may add or take away signs over time so that your train shows how your behavior cycle works for you.

_____'s Train and How It Runs

Starting Out	**Picking Up Steam**	**Point of No Return**	**Explosion**

Picking Up Steam
Behavior Description

Sometimes you will be able to get back to having a great day and feeling well regulated. Other times this will not be so, and your train will progress to the Picking Up Steam stage. It is important that you and those who support you know exactly what it looks like when your train begins Picking Up Steam.

When my train is Picking Up Steam, people looking at me will see:

_____

_____

_____

_____

_____

When my train is Picking Up Steam, inside me I feel:

_____

_____

_____

_____

_____

Activity

First, look at the example of Paul's Picking up Steam behavior in the Facilitator Manual (page 28).

Next, use your descriptions from the two sections you just completed in this workbook to write your behaviors on the green square above the green train car. If you have a lot of words in your description, you may need to condense them to fit into the square.

Finally, know that some people prefer to write their description on a sticky note and put the sticky note to the Picking up Steam square. You may either write your behavior description directly onto the green Picking up Steam square or onto a sticky note to put on the green square.

Your train will now look similar to this. Each person has different numbers of stop and go signs. That is O.K. You may add or take away signs over time so that your train shows how your behavior cycle works for you.

_____'s Train and How It Runs

Starting Out	**Picking Up Steam**	**Point of No Return**	**Explosion**
XX X XXXX XXXXX XX X XXX XXXX XXX XXX XX XX X XXXX XXXXX XX X XXX XXXX XXX XXX XX XX X XXXX XXXXX XX X XXXX XXX XXX XX XX X XXXX XXXXX XXX XXX XX XXX X X XX X XXXXXXXX	XX X XXXX XXXXX XX X XXX XXXX XXX XXX XX XX X XXXX XXXXX XX X XXXX XXX XXX XX XX X XXXX XXXXX XXX XXX XX XXX X X XX X XXXXXXXX		

| Positive Interventions | Negative Interventions |

| Positive Interventions | Negative Interventions |

| Positive Interventions | Negative Interventions |

| Brace for Explosion | Automatic Hook-Up |

| Contain the Crash | Restore the Tracks |

Picking Up Steam
Interventions

Once your behavior and feelings are those in your Picking Up Steam phase, the strategies that helped you before or during your Starting Out phase may no longer work well for you. This is common for most people who experience explosive behavior. It is a good thing to know about yourself.

Now that you know this, as soon as you see the Picking Up Steam behaviors, you and those who support you can simply move up to the next level of interventions to support you in this phase of behavior.

Positive Strategies that work well for me once I am in the Picking Up Steam phase include:

_____

_____

_____

_____

_____

_____

_____

_____

_____

_____

_____

Sometimes people who have explosive behaviors have difficulty finding the words that go on their stop signs. If that happens for you, it is O.K. It is often easier to look around and see what is going wrong around you. You might try doing this. The things going wrong are the Negative Strategies that are working against you. These can include things that are happening around you or things that others are saying or doing.

Negative Strategies that work against me once I am in the Picking up Steam phase include:

Activity

First, get out *My Visual for Outsmarting Explosive Behavior*. You will be making the third group of stop and go signs for your behavior train. Write each of the things you wrote in the red box on page 25 on a separate stop sign. If an item is too long to fit on the stop sign, sum up the idea in a few words so the words will fit onto the stop sign.

Next write each of the things you wrote in the green box on page 26 on a separate go sign. If an item is too long to fit on the go sign, sum up the idea in a few words so the words will fit on the go sign.

You may look in the Facilitator Manual (page 34) to see the example of Paul's behavior train. Feel free to use anything that may apply to your situation.

Finally, put all the finished stop signs in the third pocket on the visual labeled Positive Interventions. Put all the finished go signs in the third pocket on the visual labeled Negative Interventions.

Your train will now look similar to this. Each person has different numbers of stop and go signs. That is O.K. You may add or take away signs over time so that your train shows how your behavior cycle works for you.

_____'s Train and How It Runs

Starting Out	Picking Up Steam	Point of No Return	Explosion

XX X XXXX XXXXX XX X XXX
XXXXX XXX XXX XX

XX X XXXX XXXXX XX X XXX
XXXXX XXX XXX XX

XX X XXXX XXXXX XX X
XXXXX XXX XXX XX

XX X XXXX XXXXX XXX
XXX XX

XXX X X XX X XXXXXXXX

XX X XXXX XXXXX XX X XXX

XXXX XXX XXX XX

XX X XXXX XXXXX XX X
XXXX XXX XXX XX

XX X XXXX XXXXX XXX
XXX XX

XXX X X XX X XXXXXXXX

Point of No Return
Behavior Description

Sometimes, after using the strategies on your stop and go signs, you are able to get back to having a great day and feeling well regulated. Other times this will not be so, and your train will progress to the Point of No Return stage. It is important that you and those who support you know exactly what it looks like when your train gets to the Point of No Return.

When my train gets to the Point of No Return, people looking at me will see:

_____

_____

_____

_____

_____

When my train gets to the Point of No Return, inside me I feel:

_____

_____

_____

_____

_____

Activity

First, look at the example of Paul's Point of No Return behavior in the Facilitator Manual (page 35).

Next, use your descriptions from the two sections you just completed in this workbook to write your behaviors on the yellow square above the yellow train car. If you have a lot of words in your description, you may have to condense the words to fit into the square.

Finally, some people prefer to write their description on a sticky note and put the sticky note on the Point of No Return square. You may either write your behavior description directly onto the yellow Point of No Return square or onto a sticky note to put on the yellow square.

Your train will now look similar to this. Each person has different numbers of stop and go signs. That is O.K. You may add or take away signs over time so that your train shows how your behavior cycle works for you.

_____'s Train and How It Runs

Starting Out	Picking Up Steam	Point of No Return	Explosion

Positive Interventions Negative Interventions

Positive Interventions Negative Interventions

Positive Interventions Negative Interventions

Brace for Explosion Automatic Hook-Up

Contain the Crash Restore the Tracks

Point of No Return
Interventions

Once your behavior and feelings are those in your Point of No Return phase, it is just that – your Point of No Return. This means that you know that as soon as your behavior is in this stage, you will explode. This happens to all people who cycle through the stages of explosive behavior. Even though it is scary and nobody likes getting to the Point of No Return, it is good to know ahead of time that when you get to this stage, you will soon be having an explosion.

Please read the section on the Point of No Return in the Facilitator Manual (in the box labeled How Research Explains It, page 37) that explains what happens physiologically in your body during this stage. Your body shifts into "fight-or-flight" mode. It feels like you are literally fighting for your life and your behavior is beyond your control at this point.

Now that you and your support team know this, as soon as anyone sees your Point of No Return behaviors, they must immediately move to secure the environment to the best of their ability to keep everyone as safe as possible.

As you learn how to use your behavior train, you will become better and better at outsmarting your explosive behaviors. If you stick with it, over time you will have fewer instances of explosive behavior. In addition, most people have found that as a result of having developed their train model, when they do have explosive behaviors, they are usually much less intense.

You may talk over the next section with your support team, but because others will be acting on your behalf whenever your behavior gets to the Point of No Return, they will make the final decision on how they can best ensure safety for all concerned. Most of us who have explosive behavior like knowing ahead of time what people around us will do when an explosive episode occurs. And most of all, we like knowing that someone is able to take charge and handle the situation when we are not able to do so.

Positive Strategies to quickly put in place to keep everyone safe as soon as the Point of No Return behavior is seen include:

_____

_____

_____

_____

_____

_____

_____

_____

_____

_____

_____

_____

_____

_____

There are no Negative Interventions at this stage in the explosive behavior cycle. Instead there is an Automatic Hook-Up of the next train car. The Explosion will happen, usually in a matter of moments.

Activity

First, get out *My Visual for Outsmarting Explosive Behavior.* You will now make the fourth group of signs for your behavior train. These signs are a combination of a stop and a yield sign because at this juncture those around you can positively impact the situation by ensuring safety. Write each of the things from the red box on page 33 on a separate sign. If an item is too long to fit on the stop sign, ask your support person to sum up the idea in a few words so the words will fit.

If you prefer someone from your support team to write the items on this group of signs, you may ask them to do so. Since they will need to act on your behalf when your behavior escalates to the Point of No Return, they may want to write what they will do on the signs they will be using.

Next, you and your support team may look in the Facilitator Manual (page 41) to see the example of Paul's behavior train. Again, feel free to use anything that might apply to your situation.

Members of your support team must familiarize themselves with any policies and procedures or laws that govern their response to any out-of-control behavior you may exhibit in the various locations in which the behavior may occur. Getting to the Point of No Return is very serious.

Finally, put all the finished signs in the pocket labeled Brace for Explosion. There are no signs to put into the pocket labeled Automatic Hook-Up. Therefore, it will remain empty.

Your train will now look similar to this. Each person has different numbers of stop and go signs. That is O.K. You may add or take away signs over time so that your train shows how your behavior cycle works for you.

_____'s Train and How It Runs

Starting Out	**Picking Up Steam**	**Point of No Return**	**Explosion**

Explosion
Behavior Description

At this point, you will move into your Explosion.

When my train gets to the Explosion, people looking at me will see:

_____

_____

_____

_____

_____

When my train gets to the Explosion, inside me I feel:

_____

_____

_____

_____

_____

Activity

First, look at the example of Paul's explosive behavior in the Facilitator Manual (page 41).

Next, use your descriptions from the two sections you just completed in this workbook to write your behaviors on the red square above the red caboose train car. If you have a lot of words in your description, you may need to condense them to fit into the square.

Finally, some people prefer to write their description on a sticky note and put the sticky note on the Explosion square. You may either write your behavior description directly onto the red Explosion square or onto a sticky note to put on the red square.

Your train will now look similar to this. Each person has different numbers of stop and go signs. That is O.K. You may add or take away signs over time so that your train shows how your behavior cycle works for you.

_____'s Train and How It Runs

Starting Out	Picking Up Steam	Point of No Return	Explosion

XX X XXXX XXXXX XX X XXX
XXXXX XXX XXX XX

XX X XXXX XXXXX XX X XXX
XXXXX XXX XXX XX

XX X XXXX XXXXX XX X
XXXXX XXX XXX XX

XX X XXXX XXXXX XXX
XXX XX

XXX X X XX X XXXXXXX

XX X XXXX XXXXX XX X XXX

XXXXX XXX XXX XX

XX X XXXX XXXXX XX X
XXXXX XXX XXX XX

XX X XXXX XXXXX XXX
XXX XX

XX X X XX X XXXXXXX

XX XXXX X XXXXX X

XXXXXXX X XXXXXX XX
XXXXX

XXXXX XXXXXXXXXXX XX
XXX XXXXXX XXX

XXXXX XXXXX XXXXX
XXXX XXXXXX XXXXXXXX

XX XXX XXX XXX XX XX XXX
XXX XXX XXXX XXXX XX

X X X XXXXX XXXXX XXX
XX XX X XXXX X

XXX X XXXX XXXXX XX XX
X X X XXXXX XX X X

XXX XXX XXX XXX X XX X
XX XXXXX XXXX XX

Explosion
Interventions

When your Explosion happens, your support team (or whoever happens to be available) do their best to Contain the Crash. Again, they must be aware of policies and procedures along with any laws that apply to their handling of potentially dangerous behavior. Explosion behavior is serious. Your support team can write in below the strategies they will use to Contain Your Crash.

Positive Strategies that will be used to Contain the Crash include:

_____

_____

_____

_____

_____

_____

_____

_____

_____

_____

_____

_____

Once the crash has been contained, you will probably feel exhausted. This is common for people who experience explosive behavior. It is a good thing to know about yourself. Some people fall asleep. If you do not fall asleep, or if you are somewhere where you cannot fall asleep, it will be helpful if there is a quiet place where you can rest a bit.

It's great if you and your support team can plan for this ahead of time. In fact, you might all find it beneficial and reassuring to do a mock drill – a practice of what you will do after an Explosion. You can practice, similar to practicing a fire drill, how you will walk to the place where you will have time to get settled down. It is good to figure out ahead of time how this will happen to lessen the surprises for all involved.

The time you spend in a quiet place will help to Restore the Tracks. You and your support team may discover additional strategies that are helpful to Restore the Tracks. Your support team can write in below the strategies they will use to Restore the Tracks.

Positive Strategies that will be used to Restore the Tracks:

Activity

First, get out *My Visual for Outsmarting Explosive Behavior.* You will be making the last group of signs for your behavior train. You will use the yield signs. Write each of the things your support team wrote in the first yellow box on page 39 on a separate yield sign. If an item is too long to fit onto the sign, sum up the idea in a few words so the words will fit onto the sign. Place these signs in the pocket labeled Contain the Crash.

Next, write each of the things your support team wrote in the second yellow box on page 40 on a separate yield sign. If an item is too long to fit onto the sign, sum up the idea in a few words so the words will fit onto the sign. Place this group of signs in the pocket labeled Restore the Tracks.

You may look in the Facilitator Manual (pages 44-45) to see the example of Paul's behavior train. Feel free to use anything that might apply to your situation.

Finally, if you haven't yet put your name on the blank on the inside cover of this workbook, please do so now.

Your train will now look similar to this. Each person has different numbers of stop and go signs. That is O.K. You may add or take away signs over time so that your train shows how your behavior cycle works for you.

_____'s Train and How It Runs

Starting Out	Picking Up Steam	Point of No Return	Explosion

XX X XXXX XXXXX XX X XXX XXXXX XXX XXX XX

XX X XXXX XXXXX XX X XXX XXXXX XXX XXX XX

XX X XXXX XXXXX XX X XXXXX XXX XXX XX

XX X XXXX XXXXX XXX XXX XX

XXX X X XX X XXXXXXXX

XX X XXXX XXXXX XX X XXX

XXXX XXX XXX XX

XX X XXXX XXXXX XX X XXXXX XXX XXX XX

XX X XXXX XXXXX XXX XXX XX

XXX X X XXX X XXXXXXX

XX XXXX X XXXXX X

XXXXXXX X XXXXXX XX XXXXX

XXX XXXXXXXXXXXX XX XXX XXXXXXX XXX

XXXXX XXXXXXXXX XX XXXX XXXXXX XXXXXXXXXX

XX XXX XXX XXX XX XX XXX XXX XXX XXXX XXXX XX

X X X XXXXX XXXXX XX XX XXX XXXXX XX X XXX XX XX XX X XXXX X

XXX X XXXX XXXXX XX XX X X XXXX XX X X

XXX XXXX XXXX XXX X XX XX XXXXX XXXX XX

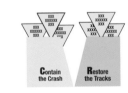

Most people who have explosive behavior find it helpful to follow a routine when leaving their quiet place and getting back into the activities of their lives. You and your support team might construct such a routine.

An example of a routine includes staying in your quiet space for a certain length of time, checking with a support person when you are back on track and ready to go, and then perhaps getting a drink of water and walking with your support person to join up with the activity you are to be a part of just then. You can construct any routine that will work well for everyone involved. It is important that you engage in this routine only AFTER you are back on track. The routine serves as a transition back into life's daily activities, but will only work well AFTER you are back on track.

This transition routine, if you choose to make one, can be written on one of the yield signs and put into the pocket labeled Restore the Tracks.

Now that you and your support team have constructed your train visual, please read the case examples in the Facilitator Manual (pages 48-50). This will give you some ideas for how you might begin to use your visual system. You may also have some good ideas of your own. Decide with your support team how you will begin to use your visual.

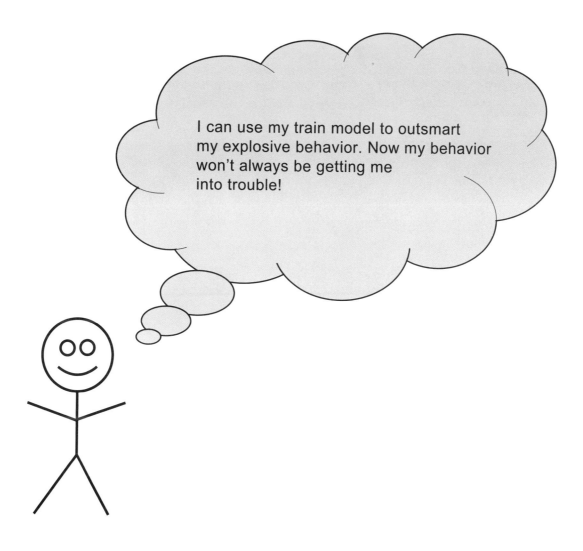

APC

Autism Asperger Publishing Co.
P.O. Box 23173
Shawnee Mission, Kansas 66283-0173
www.asperger.net • 913-897-1004